The Australian Twelve Days of Christmas

This edition published in Australia in 2009 by
Allan Cornwell Pty Ltd
cornwell@surf.net.au

The National Library of Australia Cataloguing-in-Publication entry:

13 digit ISBN 9781876711689

Cover design: Allan Cornwell
Text layout: Allan Cornwell
Printed in China through Bookbuilders

The Australian

Twelve Days
of Christmas

Conny Fechner

ALLAN CORNWELL

On the first day of
Christmas, my true love sent to me,

A kookaburra in a gum tree.

On the second day of Christmas,
my true love sent to me,

Two lyrebirds,
And a kookaburra in a gum tree.

On the third day of Christmas,
my true love sent to me,

Three magpies,
Two lyrebirds,
And a kookaburra in a gum tree.

On the fourth day of Christmas,
my true love sent to me,

Four kangaroos,
Three magpies,
Two lyrebirds,
And a kookaburra in a gum tree.

On the fifth day of Christmas,
my true love sent to me,

Five pink galahs,

Four kangaroos,
Three magpies,
Two lyrebirds,

And a kookaburra
in a gum tree.

On the sixth day of
Christmas, my true love sent to me,

Six cackling cockies,

Five pink galahs,
Four kangaroos,
Three magpies,
Two lyrebirds,

And a kookaburra
in a gum tree.

On the seventh day of Christmas,
my true love sent to me,

Seven wobbly wombats,

Six cackling cockies,
Five pink galahs,
Four kangaroos,
Three magpies,
Two lyrebirds,

And a
kookaburra
in a gum tree.

On the eighth day of Christmas,
my true love sent to me,

Eight frill-necked lizards,

Seven wobbly wombats,
Six cackling cockies,
Five pink galahs,
Four kangaroos,
Three magpies,
Two lyrebirds,

And a kookaburra
in a gum tree.

On the ninth day of Christmas, my true love sent to me,

Nine fat koalas,

Eight frill-necked lizards,
Seven wobbly wombats,
Six cackling cockies,
Five pink galahs,
Four kangaroos,
Three magpies,
Two lyrebirds,

And a kookaburra
in a gum tree.

On the tenth day of Christmas,
my true love sent to me,

Ten noisy numbats,

Nine fat koalas,
Eight frill-necked lizards,
Seven wobbly wombats,
Six cackling cockies,
Five pink galahs,
Four kangaroos,
Three magpies,
Two lyrebirds,

And a kookaburra
in a gum tree.

On the eleventh day of Christmas,
my true love sent to me,

Eleven limping lizards,

Ten noisy numbats,
Nine fat koalas,
Eight frill-necked lizards,
Seven wobbly wombats,
Six cackling cockies,
Five pink galahs,
Four kangaroos,
Three magpies,
Two lyrebirds,

And a kookaburra
in a gum tree.

On the twelfth day of Christmas,
my true love sent to me,

Twelve cross-eyed emus,

Eleven limping lizards,
Ten noisy numbats,
Nine fat koalas,
Eight frill-necked lizards,
Seven wobbly wombats,
Six cackling cockies,
Five pink galahs,
Four kangaroos,
Three magpies,
Two lyrebirds,

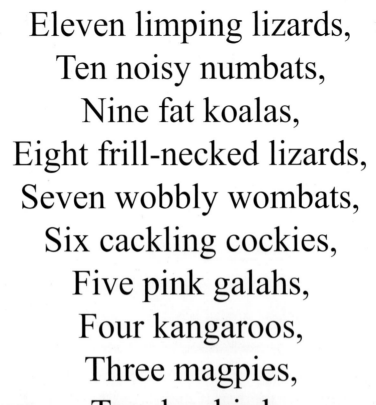

And a kookaburra
in a gum tree.

1 ONE **2 TWO** **3 THREE**

4 FOUR **5 FIVE** **6 SIX**

7 SEVEN **8 EIGHT** **9 NINE**

10 TEN **11 ELEVEN** **12 TWELVE**